Joseph
A Character Study

Ollie E. Gibbs, EdD

Study Guide

Purposeful Design Publications is the publishing division of the Association of Christian Schools International (ACSI) and is committed to the ministry of Christian school education, to enable Christian educators and schools worldwide to effectively prepare students for life. As the publisher of textbooks, trade books, and other educational resources within ACSI, Purposeful Design Publications strives to produce biblically sound materials that reflect Christian scholarship and stewardship and that address the identified needs of Christian schools around the world.

Printed in the United States of America
20 19 18 17 16 15 14   1 2 3 4 5 6 7

Gibbs, Ollie E.
    Joseph: A Character Study
    ISBN 978-1-58331-279-7   Study Guide   Catalog #MBJCS

Cover design: Mike Riester
Interior design: Bethany Kerstetter
Editorial team: John C. Conaway, Karen Friesen, Gina Brandon
Illustrations: Ron Adair, Steve Miller, and ThinkStock.com

Purposeful Design Publications
A Division of ACSI
PO Box 65130 • Colorado Springs, CO 80962-5130
Customer Service: 800-367-0798 • www.acsi.org

Contents

Introducing Joseph

What can we learn from a man who lived almost 4,000 years ago? Joseph grew up in a "normal" family environment. Then, when he was 17, his whole world was radically changed. He was sold into slavery. How would he survive? How would he act? What would guide his choices?

There were no easy answers, and Joseph was far from perfect. But not only did he survive, he has become a role model for millions of people as a man of character. The principles that guided his life are just as applicable today—because the God he served is still God today.

As we look at the life of Joseph, keep in mind that we are just like him. And just like him, we have choices to make—choices that reveal our character and build our character. Joseph's life can teach us a lot.

Unit 1

The Story Behind the Story

Choice Categories

We make choices every day of our lives. Most of our choices are short-term; that is, they are choices of preference. However, we also make choices that are long-term; that is, they have an impact on our future. From the following list, circle *S* if it is a choice that is short-term or *L* if the choice has long-term implications.

S L You choose what to wear to school.

S L You choose a book to read.

S L You choose which classes to take in high school.

S L You choose what time to set your alarm.

S L You choose which church services and activities to attend.

S L You choose your friends.

S L You choose which college to attend.

S L You choose what to do on a Saturday.

Identify the easiest short-term choice that you make and explain why.

What do you believe is the next long-term choice that you will have to make?

The Bible—Our Moral Compass

Psalm 119 is the longest chapter in the Bible, containing 176 verses. The focus of Psalm 119 is the Word of God and how it influences our lives.

Choose three verses from Psalm 119 that best describe how God's Word can influence your life. For each verse, write the reference (the verse you've chosen) in the space provided. Then write the entire verse in the next area provided. Finally, explain how this verse can influence the choices you make.

Example:

Psalm 119:*59*

This verse says, *"I have considered my ways and have turned my steps to your statutes."*

How can this verse influence your choices?
I know that I don't always make wise choices. If I focus on God's Word, I know that my choices will honor Him.

Psalm 119:_____

This verse says,

How can this verse influence your choices?

Psalm 119:_____

    This verse says,

How can this verse influence your choices?

Psalm 119:_____

    This verse says,

How can this verse influence your choices?

Understanding Ethics, Values, and Morality

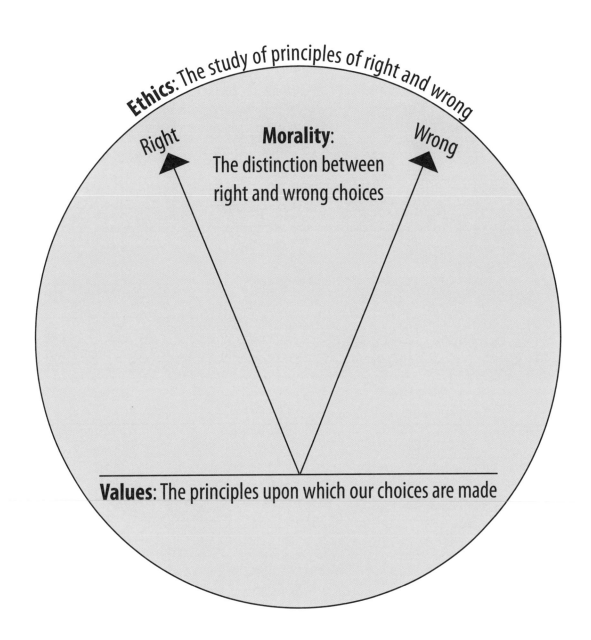

Ethics: The study of principles of right and wrong

Right

Morality:
The distinction between
right and wrong choices

Wrong

Values: The principles upon which our choices are made

Preparing to Meet God (Exodus 19:1–15)

1. Why did God tell Moses to remind the people of what He did in Egypt (19:4)?

2. How did the people respond to what God had told Moses (19:8)?

3. As a result of their response, the people would have two days to prepare themselves before God met them on the third day. How were the people to prepare themselves?

4. What is one important lesson that you've learned from this passage about personally preparing to meet God?

The Commandments as an Ethical Framework

As you discuss each of the Ten Commandments in class, write that commandment in the designated portion of the puzzle. Note that the Ten Commandments form the framework—or border—for our personal ethical beliefs.

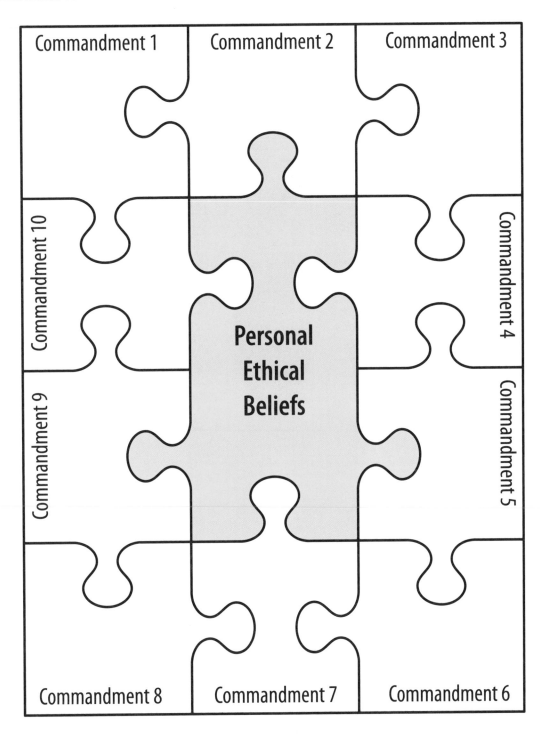

Personal Study of the Ten Commandments

Commandment 1. *"I am the Lord your God…. you shall have no other gods before me."*

Key Ideas:

Personal Application:

Commandment 2. *"You shall not make for yourself an idol."*

Key Ideas:

Personal Application:

Commandment 3. *"You shall not misuse the name of the Lord your God."*

Key Ideas:

Personal Application:

Commandment 4. *"Remember the Sabbath day by keeping it holy."*

Key Ideas:

Personal Application:

Commandment 5. *"Honor your father and your mother."*

Key Ideas:

Personal Application:

Commandment 6. *"You shall not murder."*

Key Ideas:

Personal Application:

Commandment 7. *"You shall not commit adultery."*

Key Ideas:

Personal Application:

Commandment 8. *"You shall not steal."*

Key Ideas:

Personal Application:

Commandment 9. *"You shall not give false testimony against your neighbor."*

Key Ideas:

Personal Application:

Commandment 10. *"You shall not covet."*

Key Ideas:

Personal Application:

Week 1: The Choices We Make

The Ten Commandments in the New Testament

Noted below are the Ten Commandments and twenty New Testament references. For each commandment, write the two New Testament references that address that commandment. You will note that some references are listed multiple times. That is because the reference is appropriate for more than one commandment.

1 Timothy 6:1	Romans 13:9	Ephesians 6:1	Romans 13:9
Matthew 19:18	Romans 13:9	Romans 13:9	1 John 5:21
Acts 17:29	Acts 17:2	Hebrews 4:4, 10	1 Corinthians 8:4–6
Romans 13:9	Matthew 4:10	Matthew 19:18–19	Matthew 19:18
Matthew 19:18	Matthew 6:9	Matthew 19:18	Romans 7:7

Commandment	New Testament Reference 1	New Testament Reference 2
Commandment 1 *"I am the Lord your God …. you shall have no other gods before me."*		
Commandment 2 *"You shall not make for yourself an idol."*		
Commandment 3 *"You shall not misuse the name of the Lord your God."*		
Commandment 4 *"Remember the Sabbath day by keeping it holy."*		
Commandment 5 *"Honor your father and your mother."*		
Commandment 6 *"You shall not murder."*		
Commandment 7 *"You shall not commit adultery."*		
Commandment 8 *"You shall not steal."*		
Commandment 9 *"You shall not give false testimony against your neighbor."*		
Commandment 10 *"You shall not covet."*		

God's Compass (Psalm 119:9–11)

Summarize the key points from each verse.

How can a young man keep his way pure? By living according to your word. **Psalm 119:9**

Your summary:

I seek you with all my heart; do not let me stray from your commands. **Psalm 119:10**

Your summary:

I have hidden your word in my heart that I might not sin against you. **Psalm 119:11**

Your summary:

Mesopotamia, Canaan, and Egypt

As your teacher discusses the following two questions, record important information in the appropriate section.

1. Why are these nations important to our understanding of the patriarchs?

Mesopotamia

Canaan

Egypt

2. What were the cultural similarities between Mesopotamia, Canaan, and Egypt?

Religious Beliefs

Examples of similarities for all three countries:

Examples of differences for each of the three countries:

Mesopotamia

Canaan

Egypt

Social Structure

Examples of similarities for all three countries:

Examples of differences for each of the three countries:

Mesopotamia

Canaan

Egypt

Political Organization

Examples of similarities for all three countries:

Examples of differences for each of the three countries:

Mesopotamia

Canaan

Egypt

Homeward Bound Assignment

Patriarchs–Exodus Timeline

Create a timeline that covers the period from the beginning of the patriarchs to Israel's exodus from the land of Egypt. Your timeline should include the dates for at least the following individuals and events:

Birth and death of Abraham
When Abraham entered the land of Canaan
Birth of Ishmael
Birth and death of Isaac
The Mount Moriah sacrifice
Birth and death of Jacob
Birth and death of Joseph
When Joseph was sold into Egypt
When Joseph was exalted by Pharaoh
When Moses led the Israelites out of Egypt

Abraham's Three Steps of Faith (Hebrews 11:8–19)

From the verses provided, determine each of Abraham's three steps of faith.

Abraham's first step. Hebrews 11:8–9

Significance:

Abraham's second step. Hebrews 11:11–12

Significance:

Abraham's third step. Hebrews 11:17–19

Significance:

Identifying Your Own Religious Roots

Joseph had a rich religious history. The faith of his father (Jacob), his grandfather (Isaac), and his great-grandfather (Abraham) certainly shaped his faith in God.

Ask one of your parents about your religious roots. In other words, ask your parents to identify family members who have significantly influenced the faith of your parents and family. In the space provided, write their names and a brief description of their contribution to the faith of your family.

Joseph's Grandfather and Father: Isaac and Jacob

While the stories of Isaac and Jacob contain many important events, we will focus on two of the most important events for each man. Using your Bible, answer the following questions related to these men.

Isaac's Near Sacrifice. Genesis 22:1–19

1. God told Abraham to sacrifice his son. Why does the Bible refer to this as a "test" (22:1)?

2. Abraham prepared to do what God had commanded. What steps did Abraham take as he prepared to sacrifice Isaac? What was the conversation between Isaac and his father (22:3–10)?

3. God stopped Abraham from killing Isaac. Certainly, God had no intention of allowing Abraham to sacrifice his son. So why did God put Abraham through this difficult situation (22:11–19)?

Isaac's Blessing of Esau and Jacob. Genesis 27:1–40

4. What did Isaac want to do? How did his wife, Rebekah, respond (27:1–10)?

5. What was the problem Jacob saw with his mother's plan? How did Rebekah solve the problem (27:11–17)?

6. In Genesis 27:18–31 we learn that the plan to deceive Isaac was successful. How did Isaac respond when he learned he had been deceived? What was Esau's response (27:32–40)?

Jacob's Dream at Bethel. Genesis 28:10–22

7. Describe Jacob's dream in your own words. How was the dream Jacob had similar to the promise God gave to his father, Abraham (28:10–16)?

8. What did Jacob do after he awoke from his dream (28:17–22)?

Jacob's Name Change. Genesis 32:1–32

9. Genesis 32:1–21 makes it clear that Jacob was preparing to meet his brother, Esau. Why was Jacob afraid to meet his brother?

10. Genesis 32:22–32 records the wrestling match between Jacob and an unknown man. What was significant about this event?

The 12 Sons of Jacob

Read Genesis 29:32–30:24 and 35:16–18. On the lines below, write the names of each son. (The lines are numbered to show the order in which the sons were born.)

Leah (Laban's older daughter)	Bilhah (Rachel's handmaid)	Zilpah (Leah's handmaid)	Rachel (Laban's younger daughter)
1. _____			
2. _____			
3. _____			
4. _____			
	5. _____		
	6. _____		
		7. _____	
		8. _____	
9. _____			
10. _____			
			11. _____
			12. _____

Brothers and Sisters

The questions in Part 1 concern your relationship with your siblings. If you do not have a brother or sister, answer the questions in Part 2. Regardless of whether you have a brother or sister, you do have an opinion! Please respond as honestly as you can to the questions in the appropriate section.

Part 1 (if you have a brother or sister)

1. What is one word that best describes your relationship with your brother or sister?

2. What is one positive thing that your brother or sister has done for you?

3. What has your brother or sister done that has really upset you?

Part 2 (if you do *not* have a brother or sister)

1. What do you admire most about a friend's brother or sister?

2. What do your friends complain about the most when they talk about their brothers or sisters?

3. What is something you don't like about one of a friend's brothers or sisters?

Joseph, the Favorite Son

Genesis 37:2

1. There are actually two events recorded in this verse. What are those two events?

2. What does it mean when it says Joseph brought a "bad report"?

3. Do you think this was the first time that Joseph had told his father about "bad" things his brothers had done? How do you think Joseph's brothers felt about what he did?

Genesis 37:3

4. Why did Jacob love Joseph more than his other sons?

5. How did Jacob show Joseph that he was "special"?

6. Was it right or wise for Jacob to show favoritism?

Genesis 37:4

7. What was the response of Joseph's brothers?

8. Was it right for them to feel jealousy?

9. What do you think it means that the brothers "could not speak a kind word to him"?

The Importance of Dreams

Dreams in the ancient world

Dreams in the Old Testament

Dreams in the New Testament

Joseph's Dreams

What was the example used in Joseph's first dream?

What was the example used in Joseph's second dream?

What do the sun, moon, and stars represent in Joseph's second dream?

What was Jacob's response to Joseph's dreams?

Joseph's Brothers Plot Against Him

Genesis 6:37:12–28

Story Line 1. Genesis 37:12–14a

Story Line 2. Genesis 37:14b–17a

Story Line 3. Genesis 37:17b

Story Line 4. Genesis 37:18–20

Story Line 5. Genesis 37:21–22

Story Line 6. Genesis 37:23–28

Jacob Is Deceived

Story Line 7. Genesis 37:29–30

Story Line 8. Genesis 37:31–32

Story Line 9. Genesis 37:33–35

Story Line 10. Genesis 37:36

Unit 2

Facing Temptation

Reflections on Genesis 39:2

This week's memory verse is Genesis 39:2: "The Lord was with Joseph and he prospered, and he lived in the house of his Egyptian master."

There are three important parts to this verse. In your own words, explain what you believe each part of the verse means.

Part 1: "The Lord was with Joseph"

Part 2: "he prospered"

Part 3: "he lived in the house of his Egyptian master"

Joseph's Adjustments

As you read Genesis 39:1–2, substitute your name for Joseph's name. If you had been in Joseph's place, what adjustments would you have had to make because you were now living in Potiphar's house instead of with your father, Jacob, in Canaan?

Provide five examples of adjustments you would have to make in the following spaces:

Example 1:_____

Example 2:_____

Example 3:_____

Example 4:_____

Example 5:_____

Actions of Biblical Leaders

Read the passage associated with each of the following actions of biblical leaders. Briefly explain how that action is manifested in the life of the individual noted.

Responding to the call to be a leader

Noah (Genesis 6:8–22)

Leading effectively

Solomon (1 Kings 5:1–7)

Maintaining spiritual focus

Moses (Exodus 15:1–18)

Preparing the next generation of leaders

Elijah (2 Kings 2:1–14)

Actions of Biblical Leaders

Read the passage associated with each of the following actions of biblical leaders. Briefly explain how that action is manifested in the life of the individual noted.

Responding to the call to be a leader

Samuel (1 Samuel 3:1–10)

Leading effectively

Daniel (Daniel 1:1–21)

Maintaining spiritual focus

David (Psalm 86)

Preparing the next generation of leaders

Jesus (Matthew 28:16–20)

Actions of Biblical Leaders

Read the passage associated with each of the following actions of biblical leaders. Briefly explain how that action is manifested in the life of the individual noted.

Responding to the call to be a leader

Isaiah (Isaiah 6:1–8)

Leading effectively

John the Baptist (Matthew 3:1–16)

Maintaining spiritual focus

Jeremiah (Lamentations 5)

Preparing the next generation of leaders

Paul (1 Timothy 6:11-21)

Actions of Biblical Leaders

Read the passage associated with each of the following actions of biblical leaders. Briefly explain how that action is manifested in the life of the individual noted.

Responding to the call to be a leader

Philip (Acts 8:26–40)

Leading effectively

Priscilla and Aquila (Acts 18:24–26)

Maintaining spiritual focus

Paul (Philippians 4:4–13)

Preparing the next generation of leaders

Moses (Numbers 27:12–23)

The Lord, Joseph, and Potiphar

Record what the Lord, Joseph, and Potiphar did or said in Genesis 39:1–6a.

Genesis 39:1

Joseph …   Potiphar …

Genesis 39:2

The Lord …   Joseph …

Genesis 39:3

Potiphar …   The Lord …

Genesis 39:4

Joseph …   Potiphar …

Genesis 39:5

Potiphar …   The Lord …

Genesis 39:6a

Joseph …   Potiphar …

Yesterday's and Today's Leaders

After selecting one historical leader and one modern-day leader, write their names in the spaces provided. In each column, list how things would be different if the leader had not accepted responsibility.

Historical Leader	Modern-Day Leader
_____	_____

Temptation and Sin

1. Using a Bible dictionary, a handbook, or an encyclopedia, briefly explain the difference between *temptation* and *sin*. You may also use online reference works.

2. In Genesis 39:6b–15 it is very clear that Joseph was tempted. However, did he commit sin? Whether you answered yes or no, briefly explain your response.

3. What are the three temptations that are most often faced by students your age? Write each temptation in a complete sentence.

Temptation 1

Temptation 2

Temptation 3

The Accusation of Potiphar's Wife

Genesis 39:13–15

1. There are at least two reasons Potiphar's wife called out to the household servants to accuse Joseph. What were those two reasons?

Reason 1

Reason 2

2. Potiphar's wife calls Joseph "this Hebrew." Why did she refer to Joseph in this way?

3. How did Potiphar's wife "twist the truth" in her accusation to her servants? In other words, how was her version of what happened completely the opposite of what had actually occurred?

The truth

The "twisted truth"

4. Potiphar's wife demonstrated a practice common to someone who is caught in a lie: "twisting the truth." Give an example of a time when someone lied about you by twisting the truth.

Opportunities to Deceive

1. In your own words, define *deceive*.

2. What is a synonym?

3. The words *cheat*, *double-cross*, and *mislead* are synonyms for *deceive*. For each of the three words, describe (in one or two paragraphs) a time when you were a victim of that action. The definitions for these words have been provided. You will need to write an example for each of the three words.

Cheat: to practice trickery, to violate rules dishonestly

Double-cross: to betray, to do something when you said you wouldn't do it

Mislead: to deliberately point someone in the wrong direction, to knowingly provide information that will cause someone else to be negatively affected

Reporting from Egypt

Write a newspaper article based on the headline assigned to your group. Be sure that your article reflects the facts recorded in Genesis 39. Underline at least three biblical facts in your article.

Headline #1: Potiphar's Wife Screams for Help
Headline #2: Accusations Mount Against Hebrew Slave
Headline #3: Potiphar Sends Joseph to Prison
Headline #4: Warden Impressed by Slave's Leadership
Headline #5: Prison Conditions Improve

God's Perspective

1. One of the definitions of *perspective* is "a way of seeing." What do we learn about God's perspective from Isaiah 55:8?

2. What two principles do we learn from Galatians 2:13 about God and His relationship to us?

3. Why are Isaiah 55:8 and Galatians 2:13 important to Joseph's story in Genesis 39:16–23?

Our Response

It is not only important to understand the story found in Genesis 39:16–23; it is also important to note how Joseph responded in the situation. The following three principles, demonstrated by Joseph, should also characterize our lives when we believe we have been falsely accused. Answer the question associated with each of the principles.

1. Joseph maintained an excellent attitude.

Why is it important to control our attitude in a difficult situation?

2. Joseph remained faithful.

Why do some people, when faced with hardship, turn away from God?

3. Joseph continued to practice personal integrity.

How did Joseph demonstrate personal integrity?

Case Study Evaluation

Case Study 1

How does Case Study 1 illustrate Principle 7?

Since cheating is wrong, why do so many students cheat?

What are the positive benefits of refusing to cheat?

Case Study 2

How does Case Study #2 illustrate Principle 7?

Although Caitlyn felt the pressure to stay at the party with her friends, she made the decision to leave. What do you believe is the greatest area of "peer pressure" experienced by students your age?

Caitlyn's "friends" turned against her. How would you describe a true friend?

Prisons

1. Samson (Judges 16:21, 25) and Jeremiah and Daniel (Jeremiah 38:6, Daniel 6) experienced the two most common types of prisons in ancient times. Some of the prisons were man-made; Samson was confined in this kind of prison. The other type was a natural enclosure, such as a pit (Jeremiah) or a cave or den (Daniel). Joseph's brothers also threw him into a pit.

Egypt was one of the few ancient countries that had man-made prisons. What were these prisons like during the time of Joseph?

2. Potiphar certainly could have sent Joseph to a pit or dungeon-like prison. His wife's accusation was serious and widely known. However, he chose to send him to the "king's prison," the Place of Confinement. Why do you think Potiphar made this decision?

3. The warden "put Joseph in charge of all those held in the prison, and he was made responsible for all that was done there" (39:22). What does this mean to you?

Unit 3

From Prison to Pharaoh's Court

Week 7: The Cupbearer and the Baker

Daniel and the Lions' Den

Daniel 6:1–28

1. Daniel was among the administrators who served King Darius. However, his fellow administrators did not like him and wanted to get rid of him. Why do you think they did not like Daniel, and what was their plan to remove him?

2. How did Daniel respond when he heard about the decree?

3. How did King Darius respond when he learned that Daniel had disobeyed the decree?

4. How do you think Daniel felt when he learned that he would be thrown into the lions' den?

5. How did God deliver Daniel from the lions?

6. What were the three responses Darius had to this good news from Daniel?

Moses in the Desert

Exodus 2:11–15, 3:1–14

1. Why did Moses flee to Midian?

2. In a very brief period of time, Moses had abandoned the courts of Pharaoh to live hundreds of miles away in the desert. Moses married and for nearly 40 years served as a shepherd. How would you describe the life of a shepherd?

3. After Moses had served as a shepherd for nearly 40 years, God appeared to him in a burning bush. Why did God appear to Moses in this way, and what did God have to say?

4. As has already been noted, God appeared to Moses on the mountain nearly 40 years after Moses had fled from Egypt. Why do you think God waited so long to give Moses this assignment?

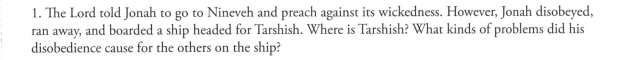

Jonah and the Great Fish
Jonah 1–2

1. The Lord told Jonah to go to Nineveh and preach against its wickedness. However, Jonah disobeyed, ran away, and boarded a ship headed for Tarshish. Where is Tarshish? What kinds of problems did his disobedience cause for the others on the ship?

2. How did Jonah end up inside the great fish?

3. What do you think Jonah thought about while he was in the belly of the great fish?

4. Jonah's prayer is recorded in chapter 2. For each of the following statements, write out the verse or verses that relate to the statement.

Statement 1. Jonah knew that he needed help, and God heard him.

Statement 2. Jonah believed that God had given up on him.

Statement 3. Jonah experienced physical terror while underwater.

Statement 4. Jonah denounced false gods.

Statement 5. Jonah made a promise while acknowledging God's power.

Dream Facts

As your teacher shares some basic facts about dreams, write the appropriate word or phrase in the space provided.

1. Researchers do not know much about _____ we dream.

2. It is estimated that a person typically dreams a total of _____ hours per night.

3. Dreams are a time when the brain consolidates _____, reviews the day's _____, or connects those events with _____.

4. For many people, the last _____ before sleep influence their dreams.

5. Some of the most common influences on our dreams are _____, _____, _____, _____, or _____.

Dream Themes

Genesis 40:9–22

Theme #1. The reference to the number three is important.

Theme #2. The reference to food items is important.

Theme #3. The reference to their heads is important.

Looking to the Stars

Question #1. What role did the stars play in the culture of early civilizations?

Question #2. What is astrology?

Question #3. What is a horoscope?

Question #4. Why is the Bible opposed to the practice of astrology?

What I Believe About Myself

The following list of 10 character traits has been provided to guide your thinking. To the left of each character trait, rank how important that character trait is in your life. For example, if you believe respect is the most important character trait for you to practice, place a *1* in the space to the left of "Respect." Continue this process until you have assigned a number to each character trait.

Now, note the character traits that you have identified with the numbers *1*, *2*, and *3*. In the space provided, explain why these character traits are first, second, and third in importance in your life.

_____ Faithfulness _____

_____ Honesty _____

_____ Compassion _____

_____ Patience _____

_____ Humility _____

_____ Serving others _____

_____ Respect _____

_____ Loyalty _____

_____ Friendliness _____

_____ Generosity _____

Silent Years in Joseph's Life

Two "silent" years occurred between the close of Genesis 40 and the first verse of Genesis 41. Although the Bible does not tell us what Joseph did during those two years, we can assume that he continued to live a godly life. The following character traits would have certainly been present in Joseph's life. For each of the following character traits, describe in 1–3 sentences how Joseph might have demonstrated that character trait during these years.

Faithfulness

Loyalty

Humility

Respect

Genesis 41:1–37 Outline

I. (41:1–7)

    A. (41:1–2)

        1.

        2.

    B. (41:3–4)

        1.

        2.

        3.

    C. (41:4–7)

        1.

        2.

        3.

II. (41:8–13)

    A. (41:8)

    B. (41:9–13)

        1.

        2.

        3.

III. (41:14–37)

    A. (41:14–16)

        1.

        2.

        3.

    B. (41:17–24)

        1.

        2.

    C. (41:25–32)

        1.

        2.

        3.

    D. (41:33–37)

        1.

        2.

        3.

        4.

Homeward Bound Survey

In Study Guide 8.1 (What I Believe About Myself) you were asked to prioritize the following 10 character traits. This is your opportunity to conduct a survey with a parent, relative, or teacher.

Ask the person you've selected to prioritize (1–10) these character traits. Respond to the two questions at the conclusion of the survey.

_____ Faithfulness

_____ Honesty

_____ Compassion

_____ Patience

_____ Humility

_____ Serving others

_____ Respect

_____ Loyalty

_____ Friendliness

_____ Generosity

What are the similarities between the numbers on your list (Study Guide 8.1) and the order of the numbers on this list?

What is one important lesson you learned during this survey?

8.5

Rules to Help You "Keep Right"

Note each of the five rules provided by your teacher. In the space provided, write a brief explanation of that rule.

Rule 1. Identify your personal core values and measure them by God's Word.
Explanation:

Rule 2. Maintain godly "inner space" as well as "outer space."
Explanation:

Rule 3. Practice careful reflection of words, thoughts, and behaviors.
Explanation:

Rule 4. Remember, you are a "walking billboard" to those around you.
Explanation:

Rule 5. Friendships are a key part of shaping our words and actions.
Explanation:

Connecting Principle 9

Principle 9 says, "When we maneuver circumstances to benefit ourselves, God may not bless us." Answer the following questions on the basis of Genesis 41:1–37 and Principle 9.

1. What does the word *maneuver* mean?

2. How could Joseph have maneuvered the situation to benefit himself in the following passages?

    Genesis 41:15–16

    Genesis 41:33–36

3. What plan had God given Joseph to spare Egypt from the coming famine?

Week 8: Pharaoh Sends for Joseph

Connecting Principle 10

Principle 10 says, "Maintain humility even in the midst of great opportunity." Answer the following questions on the basis of Genesis 41:1–37 and Principle 10.

1. What does the word *humility* mean?

2. How did Joseph demonstrate humility in the following passages?

Genesis 41:14

Genesis 41:15–16

Genesis 41:25, 28, 32

3. What was Joseph's opportunity?

Struggles of Well-Known Bible Characters

For each of the following Bible characters there is a passage of Scripture noted and two questions. For Question 1, give the first answer that comes to your mind. For Question 2, read the passage and then briefly describe the struggle that this person faced.

Moses. Exodus 4:10–17

Question 1. Why is Moses well-known?

Question 2. What struggle did Moses face in this passage?

David. 1 Samuel 23:7–14

Question 1. Why is David well-known?

Question 2. What struggle did David face in this passage?

Elijah. 1 Kings 19:1–4

Question 1. Why is Elijah well-known?

Question 2. What struggle did Elijah face in this passage?

Peter. Luke 22:54–62

Question 1. Why is Peter well-known?

Question 2. What struggle did Peter face in this passage?

Paul. Acts 16:16–24

Question 1. Why is Paul well-known?

Question 2. What struggle did Paul face in this passage?

John. Revelation 1:9

Question 1. Why is John well-known?

Question 2. What struggle did John face in this passage?

Leadership Is Not a Title

As your teacher discusses the answers to the following questions, record your responses in the space provided.

Chosen: How do we know that Joseph was chosen by God?

Equipped: How was Joseph equipped by God for his future role as prime minister?

Empowered: How was Joseph empowered by God to appear before Pharaoh?

Rewarded: How was Joseph's integrity rewarded by God?

Further Reflections from Genesis 41

Whether these questions are discussed in class or assigned as homework, seek to develop a thoughtful paragraph response to each question. Note that the answers to these questions are not specifically addressed in the passage. You will need to reflect on your overall understanding of Joseph's story to develop an appropriate response to each question.

1. How much do you think Pharaoh knew about Joseph's God (41:38)?

2. What does it mean, in this passage, to be "discerning" (41:39)?

3. Why was the signet ring important (41:42)?

4. Twice (41:41, 43) we are told that Joseph was placed "in charge of the whole land of Egypt." What do you think Joseph was in charge of?

God's Lens

For each of the following three topics, explain what the world says about the topic and what God's Word says about the topic. Be sure to provide a Bible reference to support your response as to what God says about the topic.

Topic: Stealing

What does the world say?

What does the Bible say?

Topic: Gossip

What does the world say?

What does the Bible say?

Topic: Pornography

What does the world say?

What does the Bible say?

Week 9: From Prisoner to Prime Minister

Key Words Tell the Story

Genesis 41:46–49 and Genesis 41:53–57 record the fulfillment of the prophecies revealed in Pharaoh's dreams. The following are lists of key words and phrases from these two passages. As you study and discuss these passages, record the significance of the key words and phrases listed.

Genesis 41:46–49. Seven years of abundance

Key word: thirty

Key phrase: traveled throughout Egypt

Key word: stored

Key phrase: sand of the sea

Key phrase: stopped keeping records

Genesis 41:53–57. Seven years of famine

Key phrase: other lands

Key phrase: people cried

Key phrase: go to Joseph

Key phrase: sold grain

Key phrase: countries came

Unit 4

Letting Go of Grudges

Map, Timeline, Story

The following six stories provide a summary review of the major events studied thus far. As you review these stories, record the essential information in the space provided in each story section. Be sure that you understand the relationship of the story to the map and the timeline.

Story ❶   Abraham: From Ur to the Promised Land   (Genesis 12:1–5)

Story ❷   God Provides a Sacrifice in Place of Isaac   (Genesis 22:1–18)

Story ❸   Joseph Sold to Midianites   (Genesis 37:28–36)

Story ❹   From Potiphar's House to Prison   (Genesis 39:19–23)

Story ❺   Pharaoh Exalts Joseph   (Genesis 41:41–44)

Story ❻   Joseph's 10 Brothers Travel to Egypt   (Genesis 42:1–5)

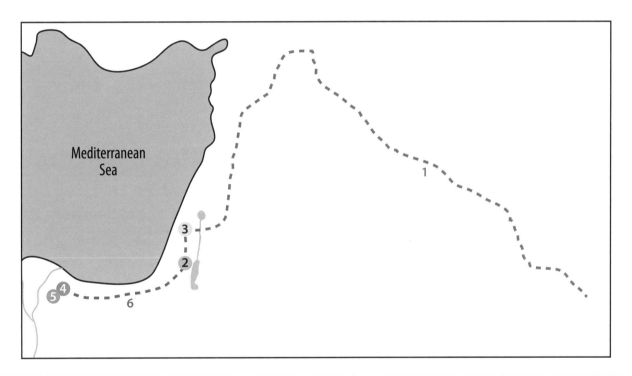

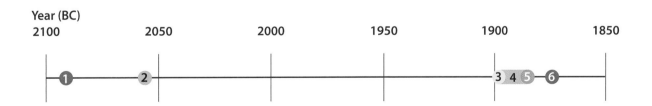

Story ❶   Abraham: From Ur to the Promised Land   (Genesis 12:1–5)

Story ❷   God Provides a Sacrifice in Place of Isaac   (Genesis 22:1–18)

Story ❸   Joseph Sold to Midianites   (Genesis 37:28–36)

Story ❹   From Potiphar's House to Prison   (Genesis 39:19–23)

Story ❺   Pharaoh Exalts Joseph   (Genesis 41:41–44)

Story ❻   Joseph's 10 Brothers Travel to Egypt   (Genesis 42:1–5)

Three Important Questions

After you have read Genesis 42:1–3, the following three questions should come to mind. The answers to these questions are *not* in the passage. Consider what you have learned so far as you seek to answer each question.

1. How do you think Jacob learned that there was grain in Egypt?

2. Why did Jacob believe that Egypt would sell some of its grain?

3. Why did Jacob accuse his sons of just "looking at each other"?

Anatomy of Jacob's Decision

Jacob made the decision to send 10 of his sons to Egypt to buy grain. *Anatomy* refers to the structure or analysis of an organism or process. We are going to analyze the parts of Jacob's decision-making process. As your teacher identifies and explains the three components of Jacob's decision, consider how the process applies in your own life.

Component #1. Realize why you need to make a decision.

Component #2. Answer the three questions of a decision.

    1. What are my alternatives?

    2. What is the plan?

    3. Who should be involved?

Component #3. Work the decision.

Which of these three components is the most difficult for you to do? Identify the component and give an example of why you have difficulty deciding either why you need to make a decision, how to make the decision, or how to work the decision.

Broken-Relationship Facts

We all experience broken relationships. While the nature of our broken relationships may not be as serious as that between Joseph and his brothers, we still need to take steps to heal the relationships.

As your teacher discusses the following facts about broken relationships, consider the broken relationships you have experienced. The choice to mend or ignore a broken relationship is ours. God is honored in our lives when we take the first step to repair broken relationships.

Fact #1. Everyone will experience a broken relationship.

Fact #2. We all respond differently to a broken relationship.

Fact #3. Restoration is possible in some broken relationships.

Fact #4. A positive response is necessary to heal a broken relationship.

Joseph's Role in God's Master Plan

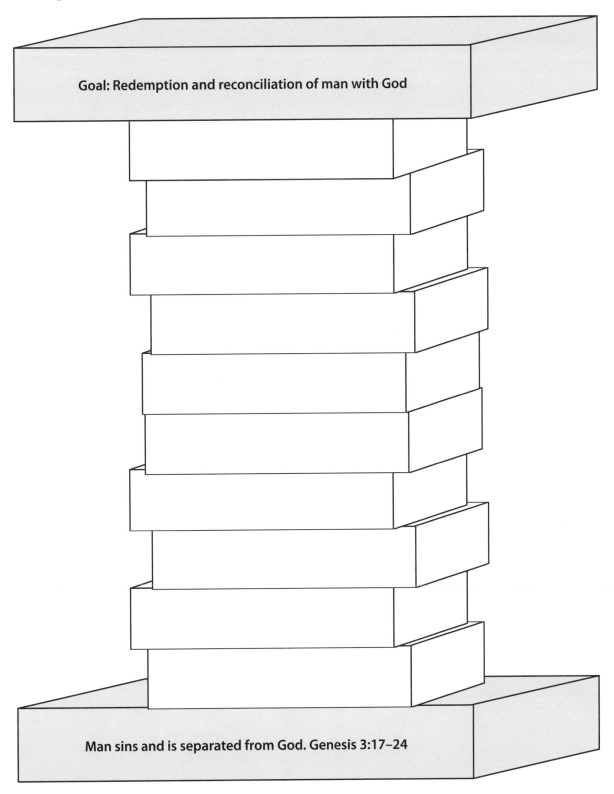

Goal: Redemption and reconciliation of man with God

Man sins and is separated from God. Genesis 3:17–24

Romans Road

Look up each of the following passages from the book of Romans. Write the reference for the corresponding passage in the space of the statement that explains that step of the Romans Road.

Romans 3:10–12, 23   Romans 10:9–10, 13   Romans 5:1; 8:38–39   Romans 6:23

Steps	Romans Reference
Step 1: Everyone needs salvation because we all have sinned.	
Step 2: Jesus Christ died for our sins.	
Step 3: We receive salvation and eternal life through faith in Jesus Christ.	
Step 4: Salvation through Jesus Christ restores our relationship with God.	

Brothers Speak the Truth

Joseph's brothers make six true statements in Genesis 42:10–13. Write the truth in the space provided by the appropriate reference.

Truth #1 (Genesis 42:10)

Truth #2 (Genesis 42:11)

Truth #3 (Genesis 42:11)

Truth #4 (Genesis 42:13)

Truth #5 (Genesis 42:13)

Truth #6 (Genesis 42:13)

Benefits of Telling the Truth

Part 1. Write a one-paragraph response to the following question: "What do you believe is the greatest benefit to telling the truth?"

Part 2. There are certainly many benefits of telling the truth. Your teacher will discuss the following three benefits with you. Record your observations about these benefits in the spaces provided.

1. When we tell the truth from the beginning, we don't have to "remember" what we said in the past.

2. When we tell the truth, we avoid the guilt that comes with lying.

3. When we tell the truth, others respect and trust us.

Actions and Reactions

Every day we are involved in a number of action/reaction situations. That's exactly what occurred between Joseph and his brothers in Genesis 42:21–28. As your teacher discusses the actions and reactions recorded in this passage, answer the following questions.

The brothers' reaction and action (42:21–22)

1. How would you describe the brothers' reaction?

2. What was the action that caused the brothers to react this way?

Joseph's reaction and action (42:23–25)

1. What was Joseph's reaction?

2. What were the actions Joseph took?

The brothers' reaction and action (42:26–28)

1. What was the brothers' reaction, and what caused this reaction?

2. What were the brothers' actions?

False Guilt and True Guilt

As you read Genesis 42:21–28 you can see the guilt experienced by the brothers. Some suggest, however, that the brothers did not experience "true" guilt. Psychologists believe that there is a difference between "false" and "true" guilt. As your teacher explains the differences, write your responses and notes in the space provided.

Characteristics of false guilt

1. False guilt focuses on self-pity and punishing oneself.

2. False guilt believes the situation is irreversible.

3. False guilt expects God's punishment.

Characteristics of true guilt

1. True guilt acknowledges behavior as sin.

2. True guilt requires repentance.

3. True guilt desires to make right the offense.

Genesis 42:21–23 Review

When placed in their proper order, the following seven phrases will complete our memory passage, Genesis 42:21–23. At the bottom of the passage, place the seven phrases in the proper order.

They did not realize that Joseph could understand them,

But you wouldn't listen! Now we must give an accounting for his blood."

They said to one another, "Surely we are being punished because of our brother.

Reuben replied, "Didn't I tell you not to sin against the boy?

We saw how distressed he was when he pleaded with us for his life,

since he was using an interpreter.

but we would not listen; that's why this distress has come upon us."

God's Goodness in Times of Guilt

Level	Reference	Observations
5	Psalm 103:11–12	
4	Ephesians 2:8	
3	Romans 6:6	
2	1 John 1:9	
1	James 4:7	

12.1

Consistent Stories

Genesis 42:9–28 reports what happened in Egypt as well as what happened on the return trip to Canaan. Genesis 42:29–35 records the story that the brothers told their father.

Look up the reference given in Column 1 and the corresponding reference in Column 2. On the basis of the content of these two references, write the similar fact(s) recorded in the two passages.

Reference 1	Reference 2	Similar facts
Genesis 42:9, 12, 14	Genesis 42:30	
Genesis 42:11	Genesis 42:31	
Genesis 42:11, 13	Genesis 42:32	
Genesis 42:19, 20	Genesis 42:33, 34	
Genesis 42:27, 28	Genesis 42:35	

Resistance

Jacob Fails to "Walk by Faith."

The response Jacob had to his sons' news can be characterized by the words *resistance*, *overreaction*, and *negativism*. Pretend that you are there with Jacob and his sons when he receives the news. You have been called to Jacob's home to serve as a counselor. Using the following questions as your guide, describe how you would address Jacob's *resistance* to his sons' request.

1. Why do you think Jacob was resisting his sons' request to return to Egypt with Benjamin?

2. As Jacob's counselor, you believe that what his sons are saying is true. You also believe that God is using Jacob's sons to reunite the family. How could you encourage Jacob to trust God and to grant his sons' request?

3. Reuben was so convinced that Jacob needed to let them take Benjamin back to Egypt to secure Simeon's release that Reuben offered the life of his own sons to Jacob if he failed. How would you use Reuben's courageous words to convince Jacob that he needs to allow Benjamin to return?

4. If you could use a verse from the New Testament to help Jacob stop resisting, what verse would you choose? Write out the verse and reference in the space provided.

Overreaction

Jacob makes assumptions that are not true.

The response Jacob had to his sons' news can be characterized by the words *resistance*, *overreaction*, and *negativism*. Pretend that you are there with Jacob and his sons when he receives the news. You have been called to Jacob's home to serve as a counselor. Using the following questions as your guide, describe how you would address Jacob's *overreaction* to his sons' request.

1. Overreaction occurs when someone makes assumptions that are not true. What do you think are some of the assumptions Jacob made upon hearing the news from his sons?

2. Typically, overreaction is a very emotional response. This was clearly true in Jacob's case. How would you have counseled Jacob during this highly emotional time?

3. What are two examples of Jacob's overreaction that you can identify in this passage of Scripture?

4. Keeping our emotions under control is very important. If you could choose a verse from the New Testament to help Jacob control his emotions, what verse would you choose? Write out the verse and reference in the space provided.

Negativism

Jacob fails to see the good that exists.

The response Jacob had to his sons' news can be characterized by the words *resistance*, *overreaction*, and *negativism*. Pretend that you are there with Jacob and his sons when he receives the news. You have been called to Jacob's home to serve as a counselor. Using the following questions as your guide, describe how you would address Jacob's *negativism* to his sons' request.

1. Negativism ignores the good that is present and dwells on everything that is wrong, or that could go wrong. While the news Jacob received was certainly not good, there were some things for which he could have been thankful. What were some of the good things Jacob ignored?

2. Negativism is a response pattern that develops over time. In other words, Jacob did not just wake up one morning and decide to be negative. How and/or when do you think Jacob's negativism began?

3. What are two examples of Jacob's negativism that you can identify in this passage of Scripture?

4. Maintaining a positive, joyful spirit is taught throughout the Bible. If you could choose a verse from the New Testament to help Jacob focus on being positive and joyful, what verse would you choose? Write out the verse and reference in the space provided.

Walking by Faith

What does the Bible say about walking by faith? Read each of the following verses. Complete each phrase with a statement summarizing what each reference says about walking by faith.

2 Corinthians 5:7	Walking by faith …
Hebrews 11:1	Walking by faith …
2 Corinthians 4:16–18	Walking by faith …
Proverbs 3:5–6	Walking by faith …
Hebrews 11:6	Walking by faith …

The Five Be's for Avoiding Overreaction

1. Be sure you know all the facts.

2. Be positive when change is suggested.

3. Be ready to learn from the situation.

4. Be appreciative in spite of what has happened.

5. Be calm even when others lose control.

Unit 5

Seeing God's Plan

Your Diary of Genesis 43

Pretend that you are one of Jacob's sons and that you are keeping a diary of the events and conversations described in Genesis 43. Each of the following five diary entry passages represents an important segment of this chapter. Write your diary entry for each of these passages, using the clarity, chronology, and commentary guidelines.

Diary Entry Passage: Genesis 43:1–10

Clarity

Chronology

Commentary

Diary Entry Passage: Genesis 43:11–15

Clarity

Chronology

Commentary

Diary Entry Passage: Genesis 43:16–24

Clarity

Chronology

Commentary

Diary Entry Passage: Genesis 43:25–30

Clarity

Chronology

Commentary

Diary Entry Passage: Genesis 43:31–34

Clarity

Chronology

Commentary

Three Questions

Answer the following questions from Genesis 43:1–15. Remember, the answers to these questions will require that you apply your knowledge of Joseph's story as well as the information provided in this passage.

1. Jacob directed his sons to return to Egypt a second time for more grain. How much time had elapsed between their first trip and this second trip?

2. Jacob was upset that his sons told the Egyptian lord that they had a younger brother. Jacob demanded to know why they told the lord this private detail about their family. Judah replied that the Egyptian lord "questioned us closely about ourselves and our family." What was Judah saying?

3. Why do you think Jacob told his sons to take gifts and double the silver to present to the prime minister of Egypt?

The Men Were Frightened

And the men were frightened
Genesis 43:16–25

"The men were frightened" could be a compelling headline for a newspaper article. Read this passage and select the five most important facts that you would include in a news story that began with this headline.

Fact #1

Fact #2

Fact #3

Fact #4

Fact #5

Joseph's Unusual Behavior

Genesis 43:26–34

1. What was unusual about the questions Joseph asked?

2. What was unusual about Joseph's hurried departure?

3. What was unusual about the order in which Joseph assigned seating to his brothers?

Adam and Eve's Test

Genesis 2:15–17, 3:1–6

Fact Questions:

1. What was the nature of the test that God gave to Adam and Eve?

2. What did God say would happen to them if they failed the test?

3. What did the serpent say to Eve?

4. What did Eve do next?

Short-Answer Questions:

1. This test took place in the Garden of Eden. What do you know about the Garden of Eden?

2. Why do you think the tree in the middle of the garden was called the "tree of the knowledge of good and evil"?

3. Adam and Eve failed God's test. What was the result of their failure?

Abraham's Test

Genesis 22:1–18

Fact Questions:

1. What was the nature of the test that God gave to Abraham?

2. Why was this a difficult test for Abraham?

3. Once the wood and altar had been prepared, what did Isaac say to his father?

4. What was Abraham's response to his son?

Short-Answer Questions:

1. According to the Bible, the location for this sacrifice was Mount Moriah. Where is Mount Moriah, and why is it significant today?

2. Abraham, the father of the nation of Israel, is described in Hebrews 11:8–19 as one who walked by faith. Why do you believe Abraham was described in this way?

3. When God saw that Abraham was willing to sacrifice his only son, He renewed His promise to Abraham by saying, "I will surely bless you and make your descendants as numerous as the stars in the sky and as the sand on the seashore" (22:17). What was God saying by referring to the "stars in the sky" and "the sand on the seashore"?

4. Abraham passed his test. What were the results of his obedience?

Week 14: Joseph's Tests

Blood-on-the-Doorposts Test

Exodus 12:1–13, 21–23, 28–30

Fact Questions:

1. What was the nature of the test that God gave to the Israelites?

2. Why was this test difficult?

3. After killing the lamb and spreading the blood on the doorframes, the Israelites were to eat the meat of the lamb. What were they supposed to do with any meat left over?

4. Moses told the people to go and select the lambs they would sacrifice for their families. What name did Moses give these lambs?

Short-Answer Questions:

1. There was an interval of about 400 years between the time of Joseph and the Exodus. Where in Egypt did the Israelites live, and what did they do?

2. The blood on the sides and tops of the doorframes was to protect the Israelites from the tenth plague (death of the firstborn). What were the other nine plagues?

3. What do you believe was God's purpose for the plagues?

4. The Israelites passed the test. What was the result of their obedience?

Solomon's Test

1 Kings 3:4–14

Fact Questions:

1. What was the nature of the test that God gave to Solomon when he became king over Israel?

2. Why was this test so difficult for the new king?

3. What did Solomon request?

4. Was God pleased with Solomon's request?

Short-Answer Questions:

1. Solomon was the third king of what we call the "united monarchy" (also called "united kingdom"). Who were the first two kings of the united monarchy? How was Israel ruled before the united monarchy?

2. What did Solomon see as his weakness when he assumed his position as king?

3. What did Solomon mean when he asked for a "discerning" heart?

4. Solomon passed his test by asking for discernment instead of wealth, fame, power, or a long life. What was the result of Solomon's request?

Week 14: Joseph's Tests

Peter's Water-Walking Test

Matthew 14:22–31

Fact Questions:

1. What was the nature of the test that Jesus gave to Peter?

2. Where did this test take place?

3. What was the response of the disciples when they first saw Jesus walking on the water?

4. Why was Jesus not in the boat with His disciples?

Short-Answer Questions:

1. The Bible notes that the storm occurred during the "fourth watch." What time of the night was the fourth watch?

2. Why did Jesus walk on the water?

3. Why did Peter call out to the Lord?

4. Peter was successful for a while, but then he began to sink. How did Jesus respond to Peter's actions?

Joseph's Two Tests

Genesis 44:1–34

Test #1: The silver cup (44:1–13)

Test #2: An even exchange (44:14–17)

Judah's confession (44:18–34)

Joseph Reveals

In Genesis 45:4–13, Joseph revealed important information to his brothers about the present and the future. As you read each verse in this passage, record the "present" and/or "future" information that Joseph revealed to his brothers. For some verses, there is only present or future information; for other verses, both present and future information is provided.

Verses	Present Information	Future Information
4		
5		
6		
7		
8		
9		
10		
11		
12		
13		

Invitations of Jesus

There are many invitations recorded in the Bible. There are also a number of invitations given by Jesus. Below are four invitations of Jesus, one from each Gospel. Explain the importance of each invitation for the occasion when Jesus gave it as well as the importance of His invitation to us today.

Matthew 4:19
"Come, follow me," said Jesus, "and I will make you fishers of men."

Why was the invitation important at the time?

Why is this invitation important to us today?

Mark 2:14
"As he walked along, he saw Levi son of Alphaeus sitting at the tax collector's booth. 'Follow me,' Jesus told him, and Levi got up and followed him."

Why was the invitation important at that time?

Why is this invitation important to us today?

Luke 9:23
"If anyone would come after me, he must deny himself and take up his cross daily and follow me."

Why was the invitation important at that time?

Why is this invitation important to us today?

John 14:6
"I am the way and the truth and the life. No one comes to the Father except through me."

Why was the invitation important at that time?

Why is this invitation important to us today?

The Fog of the Flesh

Write your passage summaries in the first and third boxes. Your teacher will provide the information for the box titled "The Fog of the Flesh."

Genesis 45:21–24
The Fog of the Flesh
Genesis 45:25–28

Unit 6

Joseph's Life and Legacy

Jacob Departs for Egypt

Genesis 46:1–27

There are three significant events recorded in this passage of Scripture. As your teacher discusses each of these events, record the information on this study guide. Pay special attention as to *why* each of these events is important to Joseph's story.

Event #1: The departure of Jacob and his family for Egypt (46:1, 5–7)

Why was this event important to Joseph's story?

Event #2: The restatement of God's promise to Abraham (46:2–4)

Why was this event important to Joseph's story?

Event #3. The listing of Jacob's sons and descendants who went to Egypt (46:8–27)

Why was this event important to Joseph's story?

16.2

Jacob Arrives in Egypt

Write a newspaper article based on the headline assigned to your group. Be sure that your article reflects the facts recorded in Genesis 46:28–47:12. Underline at least three facts from the biblical record.

Once your headline has been assigned, identify your three facts and write them in the space provided. These facts will guide the development of your article.

Headline 1: Joseph and Jacob are reunited.

Fact 1

Fact 2

Fact 3

Headline 2: Joseph prepares his family to meet Pharaoh.

Fact 1

Fact 2

Fact 3

Headline 3: Pharaoh meets Joseph's brothers.

Fact 1

Fact 2

Fact 3

Headline 4: Pharaoh meets Jacob.

Fact 1

Fact 2

Fact 3

Headline 5: Jacob's family settles in Goshen.

Fact 1

Fact 2

Fact 3

What Should Joseph Do?

After settling his family in Goshen, Joseph resumed his responsibility to feed the people. After about two years, the Egyptians had no more money to buy food. As you know, there were still five more years of famine to come. Joseph still needed to make sure the people were fed and that the food was distributed fairly.

How would you advise Joseph? What would you suggest that he do to accomplish this task?

What Joseph Did

The problem: "Give us food. Why should we die before your eyes? Our money is used up" (47:15).

1. Joseph's first action (47:16)

Observation:

Observation:

2. Joseph's second action (47:20–26)

Observation:

Observation:

Observation:

Observation:

Observation:

The Importance of the Patriarchs

The patriarchs (Abraham, Isaac, and Jacob) are referred to more than 400 times in the Bible. Nearly half of these references occur in the New Testament. As your teacher discusses the answers to the following questions, you will quickly see why the patriarchs are an important part of the Bible.

1. Why is Genesis 12:1–3 the starting point for understanding the patriarchs?

2. Why was Jacob the last of the patriarchs?

3. Why did God refer to the patriarchs in Exodus 3:1–10?

4. Why did God refer to the patriarchs in 1 Chronicles 16:16–17?

5. Why did Jesus refer to the patriarchs in Luke 13:22–30?

What Does the Bible Say About Charity?

Look up each of the following three passages of Scripture. Read each of the three statements about the Bible's teaching on charity. After each statement, write a reference that you think supports that statement. Space is provided for you to add your own comments and notes from class discussion.

1 John 3:16–18
Luke 10:30–37
Matthew 25:35–40

The Bible says that charity extends beyond one's immediate family to all who are in need.

The Bible says that we express our love for God by expressing love for the poor and disadvantaged.

The Bible says that our love for Jesus Christ motivates us to use our material possessions to meet the needs of others.

Pick a Country

When Joseph was sold into slavery, he was 17 years of age. Pretend that you are 17 years old and you have been kidnapped and taken to one of the countries listed below. Select the country where you would *least* like to live. (Remember, Egypt would certainly not have been Joseph's first choice of country to live in.) Then, identify three challenges that you would face if you were forced to live in that country.

China
Saudi Arabia
Turkey
Russia
India

Write the name of the country you would least like to live in.

Identify the three greatest challenges you would face living in the country you've selected.
Challenge #1

Challenge #2

Challenge #3

Blessings Fulfilled

Jacob's blessings on each of his sons are listed below. In the space provided, place the letter of the correct reference where the blessing was fulfilled.

After you have completed this part of the assignment, your teacher will discuss how each blessing was fulfilled. Additional space has been provided for you to take notes about each blessing.

A. Revelation 5:5
B. Numbers 32:39, 40
C. Joshua 19:1
D. Judges 4:6
E. 1 Chronicles 5:1

F. Judges 18:25–29
G. 1 Chronicles 7:5
H. Judges 8:2
I. Exodus 32:26
J. Deuteronomy 33:18–19

K. 1 Chronicles 12:8
L. Joshua 19:24–31
M. Genesis 48:15–20
N. Judges 3:12–30

Genesis 48:17–20. Ephraim's blessing: _____

Genesis 48:17–20. Manasseh's blessing: _____

Genesis 49:3–4. Reuben's blessing: _____

Genesis 49:5–7. Simeon's blessing: _____

Genesis 49:5–7. Levi's blessing: _____

Genesis 49:8–12. Judah's blessing: _____

Genesis 49:13. Zebulun's blessing: _____

Genesis 49:14–15. Issachar's blessing: _____

Genesis 49:16–18. Dan's blessing: _____

Genesis 49:19. Gad's blessing: _____

Genesis 49:20. Asher's blessing: _____

Genesis 49:21. Naphtali's blessing: _____

Genesis 49:22–26. Joseph's blessing: _____

Genesis 49:27. Benjamin's blessing: _____

Burial Practices

Answer the following questions as your teacher describes the burial practices of the Israelites and Egyptians.

Burial Practices of the Israelites

1. Why did burial take place within 24 hours?

2. How was the body prepared for burial?

3. Where was the body placed after it had been prepared?

Burial Practices of the Egyptians

1. Why did the Egyptians perfect the process of embalming?

2. What was the embalming process?

3. What was included in the *Book of the Dead*?

The Most Important Principle for My Life

You have studied 18 biblical principles from the life of Joseph. Each of these principles helps you make godly choices and decisions. Select the biblical principle that you believe is most important for your life.

In the space provided, write out that principle as given to you in class. Be sure to include the principle number. Then explain why you selected this principle and how you believe it is important to your life.

My most important principle:

Why this principle is important to me:

Sins of the Brothers

Each of the following Bible passages describes a sin of Joseph's brothers. Identify each sin and be prepared to discuss it. (All references are in the book of Genesis.)

37:5, 8

37:11

37:18

37:24

37:28

37:32

Four Final Facts

On the basis of Genesis 50:22–26, your teacher will discuss four final facts about Joseph's life. Record each fact in the space provided. Takes notes of the discussion of these facts.

Fact #1

Fact #2

Fact #3

Fact #4

Making Godly Choices

Life might be easier if the Bible provided a clear answer for every possible ethical choice we need to make. However, that's simply not the case. So how is a Christian supposed to make the right choices when faced with difficult ethical decisions that are not specifically addressed in the Bible?

Begin by reading Romans 14 and 1 Corinthians 10:23–33. Both of these passages address a problem faced by the early church: whether a believer should eat meat offered to idols.

Although that's not a pressing concern in today's culture, the principles that guided the apostle Paul's counsel are applicable to us today.

After reading these passages, choose a contemporary issue that can be morally difficult for people you know. Write a brief essay that answers the following question: How can a Christian make godly choices in this area of life?

Suggestion: As you're writing your essays, ask the following questions. Your teacher will lead a discussion of the questions as part of your instructions for the essay.
Question #1. Is it permissible?
Question #2. Will it lead to peace?
Question #3. Will it build up other people?
Question #4. Will it glorify God?